I CAN DO IT MYSELF

By Emily Perl Kingsley
Illustrated by Richard Brown

A SESAME STREET/READER'S DIGEST KIDS BOOK

Published by Reader's Digest Young Families, Inc.,
in cooperation with Children's Television Workshop

I can put my toys away.

I can do it myself.

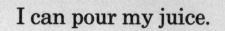

I can pour my juice.

I can button my buttons.

I can comb my hair.

I can water my plant.

I can put on my boots.

I can write my name.

I can make my bed.
I can do it myself.

I can ride my tricycle.

I can set the table.

I can brush my teeth.

I can look at this whole book.
I can do it myself!